TWISTED TOYFARE
COLLECTOR'S EDITION

NOT JUST LOWBROW TRASH

A GUEST INTRODUCTION BY ACTOR MARK HAMILL

© Steve Granitz/Wireimage.com

Never have so many toys been put to such good use!

In *ToyFare* magazine, all the Mego dolls, action figures and PVCs the rest of us have squirreled away in the basement or placed in some haphazard tableau on the shelf in the den are the featured stars of "Twisted ToyFare Theatre." And if there's a more outrageous, deliriously demented and consistently funny comic strip out there, I'd love to see it.

From its very first appearance across the bottom of four pages in the *ToyFare* Winter 1996 Special and in the more than 70 installments that have followed, it has remained a magnificent combination of contradictions. At once whip-smart and brazenly moronic, perverse yet poignant, sweet-natured but cynical, there's something wonderfully subversive to see these icons of childhood used and abused for our "adult" amusement. In this "Theatre," lowbrow laffs walk hand-in-hand with wicked pop-culture deconstruction as the mightiest heroes in the universe (apparently in between cosmic adventures) are placed in some of the most innocuous scenarios imaginable to achieve a kind of surreal comedic lunacy that must be seen to be believed. Think I'm exaggerating?

Try keeping a straight face when the majestically malevolent Dr. Doom is forced to suffer the indignity of holding a yard sale to remain financially solvent, bartering shamelessly with puny inferiors as they paw greedily through his personal effects. Watch helplessly as Spider-Man and The Hulk discover Thor working at their local Hooters restaurant in those tight little orange shorts that go so well with his flowing blond locks (which look suspiciously like the same wig they used for the Cheryl Ladd Charlie's Angels doll.) Like I said, simultaneous hilarity and pathos co-exist effortlessly as the Norse god struggles to maintain a semblance of his regal stature while slinging chili fries and Harvey Wallbangers. Somehow, I find it hugely satisfying to see such towering legends humbled by the very same trivialities that irritate us mere mortals, whether it's dealing with intrusive neighbors, annoying over-aged trick-or-treaters or an overdrawn credit card account.

In this "Theatre," the supporting characters only add to the overall goofiness as the likes of The Little Rascals, Mr. T, George Burns, Baby Spice and the cast of *The Dukes of Hazzard*, *CHiPs* and *The Smurfs* make alarmingly frequent cameos.

As an unabashed fan of this "Theatre," I have, on occasion, fantasized an episode comprised solely of figures I have personally portrayed. Based on the Luke Skywalker and Joker variants alone, they'd need a wide-angle lens. Add to the cast: Hobgoblin (*Spider-Man*), Gargoyle (*Incredible Hulk*), Maximus (*Fantastic Four*), Solomon Grundy (*Justice League*), The Trickster (*The Flash*), Dr. Jak (*The Phantom 2040*) and Wolverine (in the new video game) and you'd have a virtual epic saga of villainy guaranteed to lay you out like a Thai schoolgirl! Aw, shucks—a guy can dream, can't he?

Happy Reading,
MARK HAMILL

WE'D LIKE TO THANK YOU, MR. HAMILL. YOU'VE BEEN A GREAT *INSPIRATION.*

YOU SHOWED US THAT BROTHER-SISTER LOVE IS THE *PUREST* LOVE.

UH...SIR... YOU'RE ON FIRE.

TABLE OF CONTENTS

FEATURES

92 OFFICIAL HANDBOOK OF THE TTT UNIVERSE
Learn the secrets of the mighty (and goofy) titans of the TTT universe. *By Tom Root*

100 STAFF PICKS
Find out which silly TTT moments are the even-sillier writers' favorites. *By the ToyFare staff*

102 YOU CAN DO IT!
So you wanna make your own TTT and have us sue you for lots of dollars? These character cut-outs can help!
By Adam Patyk

EPISODES

4 HOW VON DOOM STOLE CHRISTMAS
Doom teaches Christmas a lesson in love (from *ToyFare* #6)

10 HAVE A NICE DAY
The Power Cosmic courses through...Doom's smiling face? (*TF* #10)

16 ¡VIVA MEGO!
Enjoy your visit to the Mexican Megoville...just avoid the water! (*TF* #33)

22 DEFENDERS ASSEMBLE
The Defenders need members! Does that sound funny to you? (*TF* #47)

28 THAT '70S TTT
Travel with the Megos to the era of afros and disco (*TF* #49)

34 SNOW DAY
When Bucky goes missing on a hunting trip, who's to blame? (*TF* #54)

40 WHEN HARRY MET SPIDEY
Spidey's off to Hogwarts to meet all the little wizards (*TF* #55)

46 'TIL DEATH DO YOU PART
Ever see a wedding launched into space? You've missed out. (*TF* #57)

52 DVD-DAY
The Watcher unveils a very cosmic DVD collection (*TF* #58)

58 TREK OR TREAT
The *Enterprise* crew must save the whales and go to
strip clubs (*TF* #59)

64 MEGO SUPER HEROES: THE SECRET WARS
Even washed-up '70s TV stars must compete to amuse the
Beyonder (*TF* #60)

76 THE COLD WAR
Looks like Spidey's got a Cobra
infestation—get the Raid! (*TF* #65)

82 HELLO, KITTY!
A not-so-helpful tour of Xavier's school for
bilking youngsters (*X-Men Special*)

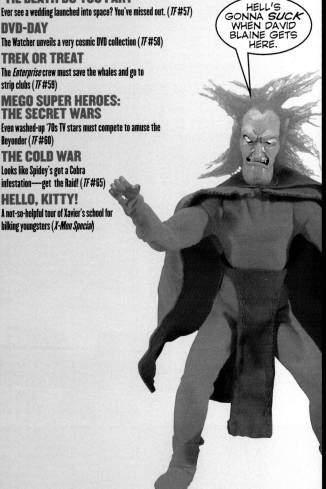

HELL'S GONNA *SUCK* WHEN DAVID BLAINE GETS HERE.

MASTHEAD

VP & EDITOR-IN-CHIEF Patrick McCallum
SENIOR MANAGING EDITOR Joe Yanarella
EDITORIAL DIRECTOR Matthew Senreich
SENIOR EDITOR Douglas Goldstein
EDITOR Zach Oat
PROJECT MANAGER Adam Patyk
ASSOCIATE EDITORS Justin Aclin, Adam Patyk
SENIOR PRICE GUIDE EDITOR Stephen Shamus
PRICE GUIDE EDITOR Jon Gutierrez
ADMINISTRATIVE ASSISTANT Cheryl Raymundo

CREATIVE DIRECTOR Steve Blackwell
ART DIRECTOR Arlene So
DESIGNERS Jacqueline Bencic, Michael A. Bencic, Darren Cruz,
Eric Goodman, Kristin Sorra
RESEARCH EDITOR Daniel Reilly
RESEARCH ASSISTANTS Jodie Westhoff, Todd Casey

SPECIAL THANKS TO ALL PAST TTT CONTRIBUTORS Scott Beatty,
Dan DiGiacomo, Andrew Kardon, Tom Palmer Jr., Robert Bricken,
Paul Schiraldi and the rest!

**WIZARD
ENTERTAINMENT GROUP**
CHAIRMAN Gareb S. Shamus
PRESIDENT & COO Fred Pierce
CHIEF FINANCIAL OFFICER Edward L. DuPré
VICE PRESIDENT/BUSINESS DEVELOPMENT Martha Donato
DIRECTOR OF BUSINESS DEVELOPMENT Robert Felton
EXECUTIVE ASST./BUSINESS DEVELOPMENT Deirdre Brooks
PROMOTIONS MANAGER Maria Capello
PROMOTIONS COORDINATOR Phil Colligan
PRODUCTION DIRECTOR Darren Sanchez
PRODUCTION ASSISTANT Meghan Lofstrom
DIRECTOR OF CIRCULATION Tom Conboy
CIRCULATION MANAGER Jen Santopietro
DIRECTOR OF SALES Stewart Morales
DIRECTOR OF ONLINE OPERATIONS Stephen Shamus
ONLINE SITE MANAGER Mike Dolce
CONTROLLER Scott Klein
ACCOUNTING MANAGER Raka Hoyt
ACCOUNTING COORDINATOR Julie Wood
ACCOUNTING CLERK Hassan Godwin
NETWORK ANALYST Jason Teitel
DATABASE ENGINEER Jeff Hannes
ONLINE STORE MANAGER Jared Cole
WAREHOUSE MANAGER Gedalias Donato

INTERNATIONAL LICENSING Alison James, Trio Marketing
(203) 266-7110 email: ajtrio@aol.com

CUSTOMER SERVICE (845) 268-3594
subscriptions@wizarduniverse.com
CUSTOMER SERVICE REPRESENTATIVE Jennifer Ali

**WIZARD ENTERTAINMENT
ADVERTISING**
VP/ADVERTISING DIRECTOR Ken Scrudato
SALES AND MARKETING CONSULTANT Seymour Miles
SALES OPERATIONS DIRECTOR Karen Evora (Congers)
SALES DIRECTOR Phil Lawrence (310) 820-0560 (West Coast)
SENIOR ACCOUNT MANAGERS Brent Erwin (NYC)
(212) 765-5700 Fax: (212) 765-5779
TRAFFIC COORDINATOR Amy Sauer
SALES ASSISTANT Jennifer Kurilla
CONGERS PHONE: (845) 268-3907 Fax: (845) 268-5386

**ENTERTAINMENT
CONVENTIONS, INC.**
SHOW MANAGER Brenda Cook (845) 268-8068
WIZARD WORLD PROGRAM COORDINATOR Phil Colligan

PRINTED IN CANADA

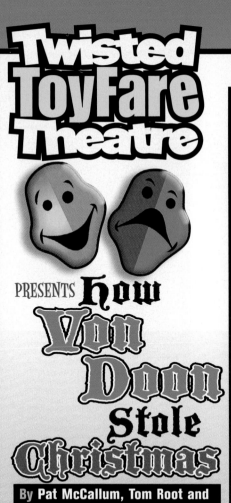

Twisted ToyFare Theatre

PRESENTS How Von Doon Stole Christmas

By **Pat McCallum, Tom Root** and **Douglas Goldstein**

Every Mego loved Christmas, they loved it a lot...

But Doctor Doom, on Doom Mountain, clearly did not!

Doom hated Christmas, despised it, detested! His fevered mind worked as the Megos all rested.

After dreaming of boxes and stockings aplenty... What if there were no presents? Not a one? Not any?

Doom's twisted mind hatched a terrible plot. He would steal Christmas! Why? Hey, why not?

With makeshift antlers atop his furred noggin Doom drafted Muffit to pull his toboggan.

His mind full of thoughts of swipe, steal and pillage Doom's sleigh hurtled down, down toward the village.

His path clear before him
his resolve resolute
Doom squeezed down the chimney
to scoop up the loot.

First victim: hulk, who lay
snoring and bloated.
"No presents for you!" nasty
Santa Doom gloated.

Then to Iron Man's pad
Santa Doom went a-lurking.
Shellhead? Unconscious, his
liver not working.

But at Avengers HQ Doom's plan became rusted
Bucky? Up. Doom's ass? It was busted.

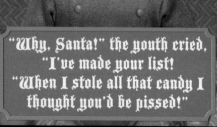

"Why, Santa!" the youth cried,
"I've made your list!
"When I stole all that candy I
thought you'd be pissed!"

"Nonsense," Doom said,
"My list? You're on top!
"Why, I'll even fine-tune
your tree in my shop!"

So with Bucky fooled and tucked safely in bed
Doom emptied the house; up the chimney he fled.

Back up Doom Mountain with mission completed
Sped Doom and his sled, the punishment meted.

"Christmas is canceled! Happy
Holidays, peasants!
"Your nonsense will cease
with no gifts and no presents!"

But Doom's rant was halted,
no words could be found
When up from the valley
came a curious sound.

The Megos weren't crying
from their pesent-less tally!
Instead, cheerful song filled
both mountain and valley.

"Where are the screams?" Doom pondered, "their groaning?
"No crying? No shouting? No bitching? No moaning?"

It then dawned on Doom, smile gracing his jaw
"Christmas...is good!" and he felt his heart thaw.

"My evil deed I'll undo!"
Doom spat like a curse
Unaware that his evening was
gonna get worse.

Poor joyriding Spidey, he never expected...

BAA-DAMM!!!

The horror incarnate as transports connected!

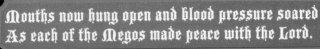

His crusade aborted, gone horribly wrong
Doom hurtled down toward the jubilant throng!

Mouths now hung open and blood pressure soared
As each of the Megos made peace with the Lord.

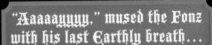

"Aaaaayyyy," mused the Fonz
with his last Earthly breath...

As he was ground into paste
under Doom's Sled of Death!

SLLURRRCHH!!!

Crushed were his hopes for toy trains and trucks
The town's lone survivor cried...

MAN, CHRISTMAS SUCKS!

THE END

Twisted ToyFare Theatre

presents

Have A Nice Day

By **Pat McCallum, Tom Root and Douglas Goldstein**

OUR STORY UNFOLDS AT THE BAXTER BUILDING, HOME OF THE FABLED FANTASTIC FOUR...

FACE ME, RICHARDS! LOOK UPON THE INSTRUMENT OF YOUR DESTRUCTION, CRAFTED BY THE BRILLIANT HAND OF DOOM!

I SHOULDN'T HAVE HAD ALL THAT CHEESE...

I'M AFRAID I'M A BIT BUSY AT THE MOMENT, VICTOR. BESIDES, IT'S POINTED THE WRONG WAY.

YOU DARE ATTEMPT TO DECEIVE DOOM WITH YOUR TOMFOOLERY?!?

SCREW IT! IF HE AIN'T GONNA TAKE US SERIOUSLY, HE CAN'T HANG OUT WITH US.

AND NO LOOKIN' AT ME BUM!

NO, WAIT! YOU DON'T UNDERSTAND! WAIT!!!

WELL, WELL! DOCTOR DOOM, AS I LIVE AND BREATHE!

WE'RE ON OUR WAY TO A SINISTER SIX MEETING WITH DOC OCK, SANDMAN AND SOME OTHER GUY WHO'S TOO EXPENSIVE TO CUSTOMIZE.

WANNA COME? "SINISTER SEVEN" STILL HAS THE POWER OF ALLITERATION!

≡SIGH≡ HAS DOOM FALLEN SO LOW THAT HE MUST ALLY HIMSELF WITH SPIDER-MAN VILLAINS?

...ALL RIGHT. DOOM SHALL JOIN YOUR... "SINISTER SEVEN."

PSYCHE!!!

TEE-HEE.

BWA-HA-HA!!

HA-HA-HA!

SAY...CHECK OUT KLAW'S CABOOSE! DAMN!

WHAT--?!? YOU'VE ALL JUST MADE THE LIST!

BAH! NEVER BEFORE HAS DOOM KNOWN SUCH RAGE, SUCH BOUNDLESS FURY! SOON ALL SHALL FEEL THE WRATH OF DOOM!

¡VIVA MEGO!

By Pat McCallum, Tom Root and Douglas Goldstein

CASTLE DOOM, HOME OF THE TYRANNICAL DESPOT DOCTOR VICTOR VON DOOM...

SUCCESS!

YEARS OF TOIL HAVE BORNE FRUIT! FINALLY--A DEVICE THAT WILL MAKE DOOM *MASTER OF ALL MEN!*

THE SILVER SURFER COMMANDS YOU TO *HALT!*

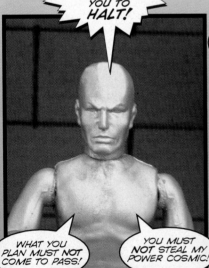

WHAT YOU PLAN MUST NOT COME TO PASS!

YOU MUST NOT STEAL MY POWER COSMIC!

THAT AND YOU SHOULD LOCK YOUR SCREEN DOOR. IT'S WAY TOO EASY TO GET IN HERE.

OH, FOR...!

EVEN DOOM HAS GROWN TIRED OF THAT GIMMICK, HERALD.

SHOO.

SIXTY SECONDS LATER...

WITH MY ENEMIES DISPATCHED AS IF THEY WERE CHILDREN'S PLAYTHINGS...*

...DOOM STANDS TRIUMPHANT!

THERE... THERE IS NO GOD! ONLY DARKNESS...DARKNESS AND OBLIVION...

...EARN...THISSSS...

*THEY WERE CHILDREN'S PLAYTHINGS.

NOW, TO RETURN TO THE TOYLESS MEGOVILLE OF THE PRESENT...

...A RETURN... TO VICTORY!

VVVVMMMMMMMMM...

SHORTLY, IN THE PRESENT DAY...

NOW, TO-- EH?

COMO SE TACO LA CHIMICHANGA.*

SI.**

*HE WEARS A SKIRT. IF HE DROPS A SOAP, LEAVE IT BE.
**AYE.

ADONDE ESTA EL PESCADO, BURRITO, BURRITO, BURRITO?*

*WE ARE OFF TO THE BEACH TO PLAY LOUD MUSIC.

ZAPATOS CON TITO PUENTE.*

...WORDS FAIL DOOM.

*HERE. BUY A MUSTACHE.

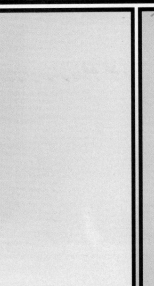

Twisted ToyFare Theatre

presents

DEFENDERS ASSEMBLE!

By Pat McCallum,
Tom Root, Doug Goldstein
and Bill Jensen

AHH... THE TWO HAPPIEST WORDS IN THE ENGLISH LANGUAGE: "OPEN BAR"!

TO: SPIDER-MAN

CONGRATULATIONS!

YOU MAY ALREADY BE A MEMBER OF

THE DEFENDERS

EARTH'S MOST FAMOUS SUPERTEAM*

PLEASE STOP BY FOR YOUR
FREE TRYOUT, ENJOY OUR
OPEN BAR AND ACCEPT A
FREE GIFT
JUST FOR SHOWING UP!

*THIS STATEMENT NOT APPROVED BY THE
COMICS CODE AUTHORITY

FREE GIFT? THAT SEALS THE DEAL.

SOON, AT DR. STRANGE'S FAMED SANCTUM SANCTORUM IN GREENWICH VILLAGE...

OH, MAN. TALK ABOUT BOTTOM OF THE BARREL.

HELLO? IS SOMEONE THERE?

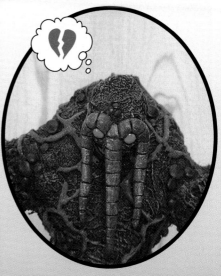

*"WELCOME TO (TITLE), (CHARACTER)! HOPE YOU SURVIVE THE EXPERIENCE!" IS ™ AND © MARVEL ENTERTAINMENT GROUP.

IN THE QUAAROG DIMENSION OF XEVOS...

MEW?

MEANWHILE, DISASTER BREWS OVER COLORADO...

ROCKY MOUNTAIN HIGH! THE CONTROLS ARE *DEAD*. I'M LOSING *ALTITUDE!*

COULD THIS BE THE *END OF JOHN DENVER?*

ONLY *ONE CHANCE...*

YOUNGBLOOD

FANTASTIC FOUR

DEFENDERS

MUST CHOOSE *WISELY!*

AT THAT VERY MOMENT...

COLORADO? PFFT!

SOMEONE DOESN'T KNOW THE MEANING OF THE WORDS "GAS BUDGET"!

THE *ALERT!* THERE'S *TROUBLE* IN COLORADO!

RUMPUS! RUMPUS! RUMPUS!

LATER, BACK AT DEFENDERS HQ...

...I REPEAT, THIS IS AN *INTERGALACTIC THREAT!* THE *FANTASTIC FOUR, AVENGERS* AND *X-MEN* HAVE ALL ANSWERED THE *CALL TO ARMS!*

Twisted ToyFare Theatre

presents

THAT '70s TWISTED TOYFARE THEATRE

BY PAT McCALLUM, TOM ROOT, DOUG GOLDSTEIN AND BILL JENSEN

MEGO UNIVERSITY DANCE CONTEST 1977
WINNER GETS $50 AND A SET OF LAWN DARTS—FUN FOR EVERYONE!

FAR-OUT!

COOL!

≿SIGH≿ IF *I* WIN THAT CONTEST, SUE STORM JUST *HAS* TO GO OUT WITH ME!

FORGET IT, REED. YOU COULDN'T GET NEAR A CHICK LIKE THAT WITH A 10-FOOT POLE.*

*INSERT YOUR OWN COSMIC RAYS JOKE HERE.

FORGET IT INDEED, REED RICHARDS!

THANKS TO I, *KANG THE CONQUEROR,* YOU DON'T STAND A CHANCE!

THE EXPOSITION CONTINUES...

REED RICHARDS MET *SUE STORM* AT THAT DANCE CONTEST-- AND FORMED THE FANTASTIC FOUR SOON THEREAFTER!

I'VE TRAVELED BACK IN TIME TO ENSURE THAT MY TEENAGE SELF WINS THE CONTEST...

...AND THE HEART OF *SUE STORM* --DESTROYING THE ACCURSED* FANTASTIC FOUR *BEFORE THEY EVER EXIST!*

* "ACCURSED" ™&© DR. DOOM

CHEESE IT, YOU GUYS, I'M TRYING TO STUDY!

TIME FOR THAT LATER! LISTEN TO FUTURE DOOM, *TEEN DOOM!* YOU AND DOOM SHALL WORK IN CONCERT TO SMITE DOOM'S ENEMIES WITH--

UM, MY NAME IS VICTOR. AND IT'S REALLY CREEPY TALKING IN THE THIRD PERSON LIKE THAT.

AND WHAT'S WITH YOUR FACE?

SILENCE, TEEN DOOM! SHOW YOUR ELDERS THE RESPECT THEY DESERVE!

GAK! GAAAAK! GAAA--

KRACK!

UMMM...

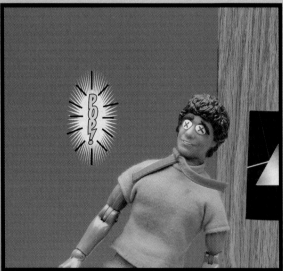

POP!

AT THE DANCE CONTEST...

OH MAN, I DON'T KNOW. I'M A LITTLE NERVOUS...

OH, STOP BEING SUCH A WUSS!

Twisted ToyFare Theatre

presents

SNOW DAY

words, pictures & plot

Pat McCallum•Tom Root
Doug Goldstein•Zach Oat
Bill Jensen•Rob Bricken

THIS IS THE WORLD'S WORST SKI TRIP. ALTHOUGH ESPN2 AIN'T BAD.

MUNCH MUNCH

...AND GO-KART #27 HITS THE BARRICADE!

LOOKS LIKE BILLY LICHMAN IS ON FIRE, REPEAT, *ON FIRE!*

WOOP-WOOP! THE MAY-DAWG IS READY FOR SOME *SICK-ASS SHREDDIN'!*

UGH. NOTHING HOT ABOUT SKI-BUNNIES IN ADULT DIAPERS.

WHAT'S THE POINT OF COMING UP HERE IF THERE AIN'T BE NO HUNNIES?

SPIDER-MAN! PROFESSOR XAVIER! I'M AFRAID THE THREE OF US HAVE DISTRESSING NEWS!

BUCKY... IS *DEAD.*

GOOD.

NO, WAIT... BETTER ACT CONCERNED.

GREAT SCOTT!

BUCKY?

OH, YOU MEAN THE KID WHO WAS JUST LIKE ROBIN...EXCEPT ...NOT.

"HULK SEE DEER! HULK PET DEER! DEER GO SLEEPY-BYE!"

"HULK! HOP! FOREST! STILL! HIPPY-HOP!"

"HULK SEE CYCLOPS! HULK PET CYCLOPS! CYCLOPS GO SLEEPY-BYE!"

THAT'S ALL WELL AND GOOD, HULK, BUT WE'RE TALKING ABOUT *BUCKY*...

AND SO...

I THINK WE CAN REACH BUCKY ON THE *SPIRIT PLANE*, BUT FIRST WE GROWN MEN MUST *HOLD HANDS*.

AND NO *GIGGLING*!

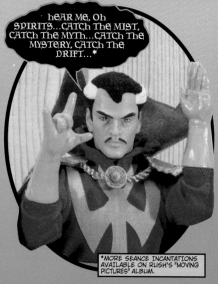

HEAR ME, OH SPIRITS...CATCH THE MIST, CATCH THE MYTH...CATCH THE MYSTERY, CATCH THE DRIFT...*

*MORE SEANCE INCANTATIONS AVAILABLE ON RUSH'S "MOVING PICTURES" ALBUM.

H-HELLO? CAN YOU HEAR ME?

WE HEAR YOU, *JAMES BUCHANAN BARNES.* PROCEED...

BUCKY?

WHAT'S GOING ON? I REMEMBER READING THE NEWEST ISSUE OF "BARELY LEGAL." THEN THE HULK CAME BY AND...

CONFOUND IT, *SCOTT!* THE WHOLE WORLD DOESN'T REVOLVE AROUND YOU!

LOOK, WE'VE GIVEN THIS A SOLID HALF-HOUR. LET'S ALL AGREE IT'S A MYSTERY THAT'LL NEVER BE SOLVED.

WELL, I GUESS ALL'S WELL THAT ENDS--*HEY, MY WATCH!*

SUCKER.

LET'S SEE IF THAT "24" SHOW IS ON. I HEAR THIS WEEK IT'S FINALLY LUNCHTIME.

THIRTY MINUTES EARLIER...

HE, UH, HE WASN'T WEARING ORANGE. THAT'S A CLEAN KILL, RIGHT GUYS? GUYS?!?

RHAARGHHH! LEAVE HULK 'LONE! HULK'S PLATE FULL OF OWN PROBLEMS!

END

Twisted ToyFare Theatre

presents

WHEN HARRY MET SPIDEY

BY

PAT McCALLUM, TOM ROOT, ZACH OAT, DOUG GOLDSTEIN, BILL JENSEN, ROB BRICKEN

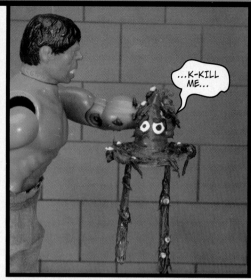

*NOT TO BE CONFUSED WITH ALL YOUR MAXX, YOUNGBLOOD AND VALIANT FAVORITES, *FREE* IN EVERY "WIZARD: THE COMICS MAGAZINE" BACK ISSUE!

THE QUDDITCH FIELD...

GIGGLE GO BEATERS!

I WAS IN "DIE HARD."

STOP TALKINK TO ME.

OH BOY, QUIDDITCH DAY! I CAN'T GET THE SMILE OFF MY FACE!

WHOOSH!

GAH!

...EVERY TIME...

SHUNK!

GIVE IT BACK, MUDBLOOD.

"AND AWAY WE GO..."

AH, THE HELL WITH THIS...

SAY...

...WHERE'S YOUR SCAR? AND FOR THAT MATTER, WHY ARE YOU DRESSED LIKE SPIDER-MAN? AND THIRTY?

WHERE THE DEVIL IS THE REAL HARRY POTTER?

NUMBER 4 PRIVET DRIVE, THE CUPBOARD UNDER THE STAIRS...

HARRY! WHAT IS THAT STINK?

ANSWER ME, YOU LITTLE TARD!

END

Twisted ToyFare Theatre

presents

'Til DEATH DO YOU PART

BY
PAT McCALLUM , TOM ROOT, DOUG GOLDSTEIN, ZACH OAT, ROB BRICKEN & BILL JENSEN

"REED AND SUE RICHARDS' QUICKIE '77 VEGAS MARRIAGE NEVER OFFICIAL..."

PERFECT!

THIS WEDDING IS *JUST* THE OPPORTUNITY DOOM HAS BEEN WAITING FOR TO EXACT HIS REVENGE UPON THE *ACCURSED FANTASTIC FOUR!*

MWAH-HA-HA- WAIT...DOOM DOESN'T HAVE A *THING* TO WEAR!

CURSE YOU, RICHARDS!

MEANWHILE...

WHAT'S THE *CHEAPEST* THING ON THE FF BRIDAL REGISTRY?

WELL, THE SALAD TONGS ARE SIX DOLLARS.

SOLD!

RHARGH! TONG, TA-TONG-TONG-TONG!

MACY'S

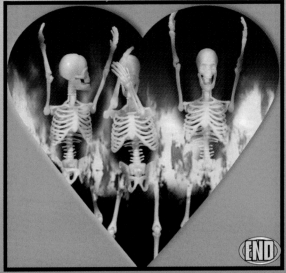

presents

DVD-DAY

BY PAT MCCALLUM, TOM ROOT, DOUG GOLDSTEIN, ZACH OAT, ROB BRICKEN & BILL JENSEN

PREVIOUSLY ON "DRAGON BALL Z"...

...JEEZ, WHO THE HELL KNOWS?

I HEAR YA.

FORSOOTH! THE ODINSON RETURNS WITH TIDINGS OF XBOX JOY!

T'WAS PURCHASED FOR ITS DVD CAPABILITIES!

YEAH? SO YOU PAID $399 FOR THE XBOX AND ANOTHER $30 FOR THE DVD ADD-ON WHEN A REGULAR DVD PLAYER WOULDA JUST COST YA $199?

...AYE, AND YON MIDGARDIAN CLERK LIED.

THERE BE NO "CRASH BANDICOOT" FOR THE SYSTEM.

BUT ALL IS NOT LOST, FRIEND SPIDER-MAN!

THE THUNDER GOD HATH JOINED A "DVD OF THE MONTH" CLUB!

"BLACK BOLT DOWN"... "SNOW WHITE AND THE SEVEN WORFS"... "BATMAN FOREVER"?

THOR, THESE ARE ALL TERRIBLE.

HMMM... NOT GEORGE CLOONEY'S FINEST HOUR.

THE PERFECT STORMTROOPER

CROM! I MEAN...OOKLA, ARIEL, RIDE!

HITHER MOVIE FEATURES POLITICAL INTRIGUE WITH HIP '70S FUNK SOUNDTRACK!

THE FALCON & THE SNOWMAN

OR LET US WATCH THE ETERNIA TRILOGY!

"HE-MAN IN THE IRON MASK." "MER-MAN WITH THE GOLDEN GUN" AND "ORKO II: ELECTRIC BOOGALOO."

DID YOU BUY THESE AT ARBY'S OR SOMETHING?

HERE'S ANOTHER ONE..."THE MOSSMAN PROPHECIES."

ARE YOU HOLDING... TIC-TACS?

NOPE.

GUM?

UH-UH.

PEZ?

WHO IS THIS?

...ISN'T MOSS-MAN JUST BEAST-MAN COVERED IN GLUE AND ROLLED IN FELT?

AND I THOUGHT US MEGOS WERE HORRIBLE TOYS.

Citizen Kang

LET'S WATCH...ACTUALLY, NO, LET'S NOT.

TREK OR TREAT

BY PAT McCALLUM, TOM ROOT, DOUG GOLDSTEIN, ZACH OAT & ROB BRICKEN

CAPTAIN? HE'S BACK AGAIN...

ALL RIGHT, *SPACE LINCOLN*... WHAT'S YOUR GAME?

I'M THE CAPTAIN OF SEXUAL HARASSMENT ON *THIS* SHIP!

YOU'VE GOT IT ALL *WRONG*, KIRK! I...UH...I CAME TO *WARN* YOU!

YOU'VE GOT TO...UMMM...*TIME TRAVEL* BACK TO THE YEAR 2002 AND SAVE THE UH...WHALES! *YES*, THE *WHALES!*

OR THE UNIVERSE IS *DOOMED!*

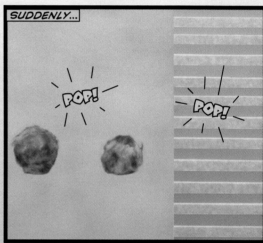

AT THAT VERY MOMENT, AT AVENGERS MANSION...

E-C-W!

E-C-W!

COME ON, *HANK*...SLUG HER LIKE YOU'VE GOT A DRINK IN YA!

POP!

CASTLE DOOM...

MWAH-HA-HA!

FINALLY, I--*DR. DOOM*-- HAVE CREATED THE ULTIMATE SANDWICH!

NOW TO GET SOME *SUN CHIPS* AND--

POP!

AND THE SCENE IS REPEATED ACROSS THE GLOBE AS THE WORLD'S GREATEST HEROES AND VILLAINS *VANISH* IN A FLASH OF LIGHT. *BUT TO WHERE?*

FIND OUT IN THIRTY DAYS WITH THE *FIRST* DOUBLE-SIZED "TWISTED TOYFARE THEATRE"...*EVER!*

NOT A HOAX!
NOT A DREAM!
NOT AN IMAGINARY TALE!

MEGO SUPER HEROES
THE SECRET WARS

TOYFARE #60
6/12/02

MEGO SUPER HEROES
THE SECRET WARS

GOD HELP ME...
EVEN DORMAMMU'S
HEAD REMINDS
ME OF PIE!

IF IT'S A
SECRET, WHY ARE YOU
TELLING US?

WINNER: PUNISHER

BADMINTON: ANT-MAN VS. THE HULK!

WINNER: HULK

KICKBALL: TEAM SPIDEY VS. TEAM DOOM!

GALACTUS HUNGERS FOR A PIT-CHER, NOT A BELLY ITCH-ER!

AM I UP?

BOY, WINNING THAT PONTIAC AZTEK SSSURE WOULD BE SSSWEET!

I'D BE THE TOASSST OF THE TOWN...

I LOVE YOUR CAR!

I WON IT IN KICKBALL!

HEADS UP!

WHIZZZZ!

WHACK!

POIT!

GO, GO, GECKO-REGENERATION!

WOO-WOO-WOO!

RUN, SWAMP THING, RUN!

LONDON, ENGLAND

HELLO, I'M *ALAN MOORE.*

CONFUSING THE MARVEL CHARACTER *"MAN-THING"* WITH THE DC CHARACTER *"SWAMP THING"* IS A COMMON MISTAKE, BUT IN FACT, THE CREATURES ARE QUITE DIFFERENT.

ALLOW ME TO ELABOR--

WHIZZZZ!

WHACK!

SCRABBLE: MR. FANTASTIC VS. DR. DOOM!

"DISFIGUREMENT."

AND *THAT'S* 52 POINTS.

CURSE YOU, RICHARDS!

DOOM WANTED TO PLAY *"YAHTZEE."*

WINNER: MR. FANTASTIC

NO CONDIMENTS? GOOD THING I SWEAT BUTTER...

Y'KNOW, THIS COSTUME AIN'T HALF BA--

WE NEED TO SPIKE RATINGS AGAIN. TRY THIS ONE ON.

...A HOODIE?

WAITAMINIT... THIS IS FROM MARTHA STEWART'S K-MART LINE!

WINNER: TIMMY

BASKETBALL: HUGGY BEAR VS. FREDDIE "BOOM BOOM" WASHINGTON!

NO, WE'RE NOT RACIST. HUGGY & BOOM-BOOM ARE JUST REALLY GOOD AT BASKETBALL.

MINIATURE GOLF: CONAN VS. RICK JONES!

WINNER: DRAW

POULTRY BATTLE: IRON CHEF MORIMOTO VS. REDWING!

WINNER: IRON CHEF MORIMOTO, WHO TODAY PREPARED FIVE DISHES, INCLUDING BROILED REDWING A L'ORANGE SERVED OVER A BED OF RICE

TONY HAWK 3: KANG VS. SPIDER-MAN!

BAD NEWS, SPIDEY...YOUR NEW COSTUME IS A SALES *TRAIN WRECK*.

WE'RE GONNA GO WITH *"SPIDER-MAN RED"* AND *"SPIDER-MAN BLUE."*

'SUP.

WORD, MY BRUTHA.

DIDN'T CORPORATE AMERICA LEARN *ANYTHING* FROM *NEW COKE?* YOU CAN'T MESS WITH A *CLASSIC*.

I'M OUT OF HERE.

IF ANYBODY NEEDS ME, I'LL BE READING *"ULTIMATE SPIDER-MAN."**

*OH, THE IRONY!

FINALLY...

AND SO IT HAS BEEN *DECIDED!*

THE *WINNERS* OF THE SECRET WARS ARE...

...*TEAM DOOM!*

YES!

TOTAL VICTORY BELONGS TO...*DOOM!*

EAT IT, RICHARDS!

THE LOSERS SHALL FLY HOME UPON THE CITY OF *DENVER*.*

...IS THAT GOOD?

...

*OKAY...WE MADE UP EVERYTHING ELSE IN THIS STRIP, BUT THAT ACTUALLY HAPPENED IN THE REAL *"SECRET WARS"* COMIC BOOK. HONEST.

TO THE VICTORS GO THE PONTIAC AZTEK...*AND* YOUR TEAM ADVANCES TO THE *NEXT* BRACKET!

...*WHAT?*

YOU SAID NOTHING OF ANY *"BRACKET."* WHO WOULD NOW *DARE* CHALLENGE DOO--

Twisted ToyFare Theatre

PRESENTS

The Cold War

BY: McCALLUM, ROOT & OAT

WITH: ACLIN, BRICKEN, PATYK & GUTIERREZ

EDITORS: SENREICH & GOLDSTEIN

MUNCH MUNCH

MUNCH MUNCH

I DON'T KNOW WHERE THIS STRIP IS GOING, BUT I HATE IT.

...OH, NO.

I'VE SEEN ENOUGH "TOM & JERRY" CARTOONS TO KNOW, THIS *ISN'T* A GOOD THING.

Twisted ToyFare Theatre

PRESENTS

Hello Kitty

BY:
McCALLUM, ROOT & OAT

WITH:
ACLIN, BRICKEN, PATYK & GUTIERREZ

EDITORS:
SENREICH & GOLDSTEIN

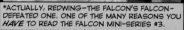

ABSOLUT IRON MAN

THE OFFICIAL HANDBOOK OF THE
TWISTED
TOYFARE THEATRE
UNIVERSE
VOL. 1

SPIDER-MAN

Height: 7 3/4 inches

Weight: 2.2 oz.

Base of Operations: Sofa

Known Relatives: May Parker (aunt); Ben Serpentor (uncle)

Group Affiliation: None

Favorite Food: The same bag of Lay's Potato Chips he's been eating for 75 issues

First Appearance: "Spider Macarena," *ToyFare Winter Special Edition*, 1996

Died: "¡Viva Mego!", *ToyFare* #33

Died: "'Til Death Do You Part," *ToyFare* #57

History: Spider-Man has certainly mellowed over the years. In his youth, he was known to splatter Jawas with a mallet to amuse himself, or take on the entire Borg collective armed with only a garden hose. These days, Spidey's much more apt to go with the flow. An army of Cobra troops living in his walls? Fine. Whisked away to an island by the all-powerful Beyonder to compete in blood sport against his comrades? Whatever. It takes an extreme annoyance to spur Spidey to action, but when it happens, he always comes out on top. To paraphrase Mark Waid, if Mego Spidey had a mutant power, it'd be "winning." Or maybe that was Kurt Busiek. We can't remember.

Known Powers: Spider-Man is just an average joe. If you want to see a superhero with the proportional strength of a spider who scales walls, read the comic books. However, he does possess the fabled "Spider-Sense," which more often than not just turns out to be "Common Sense."

Weapons: No web-shooters here, but Mego Spidey is a mean shot with the aforementioned garden hose and he's not timid about using a Shop-Vac to clean up pesky foes. Hey, that kind of rhymes!

TOYFARE #40: "A Real American Hero"

TOYFARE #46: "Fear And Loathing In Eternia"

DOCTOR DOOM

Height: 7 3/4 inches

Weight: 4.7 oz.

Base of Operations: Castle Doom, in the suburb of Latveria

Known Relatives: Cynthia Von Doom (mother, trapped in Hell)

Group Affiliation: None

Turn-Offs: Halloween; Christmas; small, white, armless robots

First Appearance: "Super Villain Jeopardy," *ToyFare* #1, Sept. 1997

Died: "Halloween At Castle Doom," *ToyFare* #4 (presumably)

Died: "Y2K Monkey Business!", *ToyFare* #29

Died: "¡Viva Mego!," *ToyFare* #33

Died: "That '70s TTT," *ToyFare* #49

Died: "'Til Death Do Us Part," *ToyFare* #57

Origin: "Hero of the Beach! Or How Reed Made A Doctor Out of Doom!", *Twisted ToyFare Theatre* Vol. 2

History: Victor Von Doom was a promising young student at Megoville University, until his Menudo-esque good looks were destroyed by fellow classmate Reed Richards' carelessness. After donning piping-hot armor, Doom dedicated his life to destroying Richards and the rest of the Fantastic Four. To date, his efforts have only backfired: a fact-finding mission at a theme park resulted in severe psychological trauma thanks to a randy robot named H.E.R.B.I.E.; a Y2K virus he thought would end Richards resulted in a stray satellite falling on his head; even his plan to interrupt the wedding of Richards and Sue Storm was foiled when he accidentally shot himself into the sun. His only successes have been at killing past versions of himself (which he's done twice), but even in his darkest hour—of which he's had many—Doom will never, ever give up his plans of revenge for those unlucky souls on his "list." He's also won an Academy Award.

Known Powers: Doom is a genius. He can *make* whatever powers he needs. So far, attempts to master the black arts, as in comic book continuity, have only resulted in catching his cat on fire. Which pleased him.

Weapons: Doom can launch deadly energy blasts from his gauntlets, and has created a variety of technologically advanced devices in order to wage war on his foes. These include, but are not limited to, the Spice Girl-projecting Spice Cannon, the '70s Smiley Face Machine, and his Baxter Building Launcher, which he uses frequently.

TOYFARE #31: "Working For The Man"

HULK

Height: 7 1/8 inches

Weight: 2.7 oz.

Known Relatives: She-Hulk (cousin); Mr. Fixit (relation unknown)

Group Affiliation: Defenders

Weakness: Monkeys

First Appearance: "Halloween at Castle Doom!" *ToyFare* #4, Dec. 1997

Died: "Jolt to the System," *ToyFare* #13

Died: "¡Viva Mego!", *ToyFare* #33

Died: "Craptus Interruptus," *ToyFare* #48 (presumably)

Died: "'Til Death Do You Part," *ToyFare* #57

History: The Hulk is forever a victim of circumstance. Whether drinking a case of Jolt Cola sends him on a caffeine-fueled rampage or whether his own bowels force him into unfortunate circumstances involving hot tubs or manhole covers, the Hulk is never really to blame for his misdeeds. This good-natured, playful soul is a true extrovert who treasures his compatriots and is always looking to make new friends. Sometimes his new friends are backing away from a bout of gamma-radiated flatulence, other times they're bitten in half by sharks, but nobody can deny that the Hulk's intentions are pure.

Known Powers: The Hulk possesses super strength and endurance, and his hide is nearly impenetrable. The greatest threat to his safety is often his own intestinal tract; if he can't find bathroom facilities in time, the results are always explosive and often deadly.

Weapons: Some might say his heart of gold. Others might point to his sphincter of doom.

TOYFARE #12: "On The Road"

TOYFARE #28: "The Mego Witch Project"

FRANKLIN RICHARDS

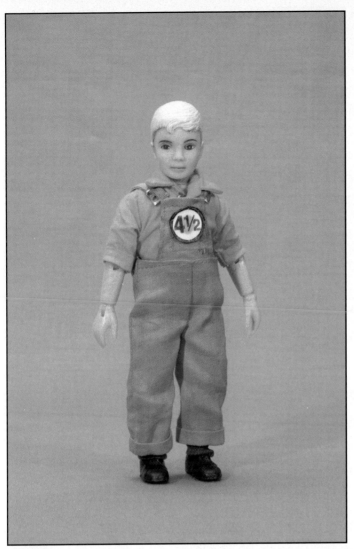

Height: 6 1/4 inches
Weight: 1.7 oz.
Known Relatives: Susan Richards (mother); Unknown (father); Johnny Storm (uncle)
Hobbies: Playing dress-up, eating candy, torturing small animals
Group Affiliation: Fantastic Four
First Appearance: "Working for the Man!", *ToyFare* #31
Died: "Working for the Man!", *ToyFare* #31
Died: "¡Viva Mego!", *ToyFare* #33
Died: "'Til Death Do Us Part," *ToyFare* #57
Died: "A Lizard in Every Pot," *ToyFare* #68
History: It's safe to say that Franklin does not play well with others. Frequently left in the care of a revolving cast of babysitters while his parents either fight crime, promote world peace or shop, Franklin has had to learn to create his own fun. Such fun might including tossing coins off skyscrapers that pierce the skulls of old ladies, or making his uncle, the ever-lovin' blue-eyed Thing, dance for him by unloading his revolvers at his uncle's feet. Franklin's only friends are the soulless automaton H.E.R.B.I.E. and the equally soulless Mr. Buttons, his teddy bear. A trial run with a pint-size Mego Pal ended in violence. In fact, most of Franklin's escapades end in violence. There's just something about that sneering pout that makes you want to...er, hug him. It is only right to hug children.
Known Powers: None, unless the power to make adults want to rip off their own ears to escape his persistent whining is a power.
Weapons: Franklin has the entire, incredible arsenal of the Fantastic Four at his disposal. As soon as he's able to reach the buttons, Megoville is in big trouble.

TOYFARE #51: "Weapon ECHHHH!"

TOYFARE #57: "'Till Death Do Us Part"

X-MEN

History: Born with incredible mutant powers, the X-Men forever fight to defend a world that hates and fears them. Well, in theory. In reality, they're more concerned with collecting paychecks from their movie franchise and picking fights with other, less cool superteams. They're kind of jerks.

Appearances: The X-Megos first appeared on the cover of *ToyFare*'s first-ever issue, the Winter Special Edition, before the magazine was even monthly. Their Famous Covers counterparts doubled for them in the landmark "Clash of the Titans" two-parter in *ToyFare* #8-#9. But it wasn't until *ToyFare* #21's "House Party" that the true X-Men were featured in "Twisted ToyFare Theatre." Since then, the X-Men have made several starring turns in "TTT," but more often, they're used where they're most needed: filling out big crowd scenes.

TOYFARE #60: "Mego Super Heroes: The Secret Wars"

PROFESSOR X
Once, there were only two things in his life that mattered: his voluminous hair, and dancing. Tough break, Professor.

CYCLOPS
He must forever wear ruby quartz glasses to keep his lethal optic rays in check. Gee, big sacrifice. Give us the optic blasts any day.

PHOENIX
She once murdered 5 billion souls in the blink of—whoa, check out those hooters!

WOLVERINE
He's the best there is at what he does. Just ask him.

COLOSSUS
Each fist wields the power of 10 Stalins!

STORM
On those long photo shoot nights, we really wish this Mego looked more like Halle Berry.

NIGHTCRAWLER
With an explosive "Bamf!" Nightcrawler disappears, leaving behind only a foul cloud. Our magazine's creative director is the same way.

ICEMAN
This Mego sucks and we made it in five minutes. Enjoy!

VEHICLES

AVENGERS QUINJET

First Appearance: "The Hunt for Red Ork-tober," *ToyFare* #62

History: The Avengers Quinjet has always ranked as the coolest of all superhero vehicles. (Screw you, Bat-mobile!) While other teams travel around in floating Tupperware dishes like the Fantastic Four (and in the Megoverse, that's literally true), the Quinjet is legitimately bad-ass. It also fulfills a valuable secondary purpose, as in both its "Twisted ToyFare Theatre" appearances to date it has landed on hapless bystanders, crushing them. Now that's comedy. It's even funnier when it's Franklin Richards and the Lizard dressed in an Evel

Knievel outfit ("A Lizard in Every Pot," *ToyFare* #68).

Weapons: The Quinjet has thus far demonstrated no mounted artillery of air-to-air or air-to-surface capability, but its sturdy construction by military contractor Fisher-Price lends itself to smooshing people.

HEY...THAT'S A *HANDICAPPED* SPACE! YOU CAN'T PARK THERE!

IT'S OKAY. I'M A SUPERHERO.

TOYFARE #68: "A Lizard In Every Pot"

I LOVE YOUR CAR!

I WON IT IN KICKBALL!

HEADS UP!

TOYFARE #60: "Mego Super Heroes: The Secret Wars"

PONTIAC AZTEK

First Appearance: "Mego Super Heroes: The Secret Wars," *ToyFare* #60

History: The Aztek's first and only appearance was as a prize promised to the winning team of the Beyonder's "Secret Wars," pitting Mego against Mego in a duel to the death! However, it was the Lizard who most coveted the shiny new Pontiac, and the distraction of the prize led to his downfall. While playing right field in a kickball game—to the death!—the Lizard let his guard down due to his Aztek daydreams, and his head was knocked clean off his body by the kickball. The Lizard lost the Aztek, but later, he tried to build his own using lots of aluminum foil and a 10-speed bike. Impress the chicks, it did not.

Weapons: With an MSRP starting at just $21,470, the Aztek's 3.4-liter 3400

SFI V6 with 4-speed transmission pales next to its VersaTrak™ all-wheel drive capabilities. Also has cup holders big enough to support Big Gulp, Super Big Gulp and, yes, even *Double Gulp* soft drink receptacles.

STAFF PICKS

SOME OF THE 'TTT' CREATORS' FAVORITE MOMENTS

Sure, it doesn't really matter what *we* think of "Twisted ToyFare Theatre"—it's what you, the readers, think that counts. But these are the "TTT" sequences that hold a special place in our hearts, either because we have some kind of behind-the-scenes story to tell or simply because they're so damn funny. Man, we crack ourselves up.

MATT SENREICH
(*ToyFare* Editorial Director)
"THE GREAT JAWA HUNT"
(ToyFare #2)

MATT SAYS: "Violence at its best and in its earliest 'TTT' incarnation! You can't help but laugh when Spider-Man decides to squash Jawas with Thor's hammer because they're just annoying little bugs. But what makes this one panel so special is the personalizing of the bloody horror that Spider-Man is inflicting upon these Jawas, with that one Jawa exclaiming aloud the death of his best friend, who is apparently named 'Carl.' Ah...giving the Jawa a name. Genius."

TOM ROOT ("TTT" Scripter/Storyboarder)
"THAT '70S TTT" (ToyFare #49)

TOM SAYS: "Not only does this sequence still crack me up, it was a blast to shoot. [Editor-in-Chief] Pat McCallum and I were tired of tying figures in place with fishing line, so we would just stand Professor X in whatever dancing position we wanted, then pull our hands away really fast. It would be up to [then-photographer] Paul Schiraldi to snap the photos in the instant before the toy fell over. It probably took 30 tries to get five usable shots. The joke here of course is that in his glory days, Professor X loved dancing and he loved his big hair. When we later cut back to the present day, the Prof is so despondent about losing both his greatest joys that he blows his own head off. Hmm. Maybe it was funnier in the storyboards."

DOUG GOLDSTEIN (*ToyFare* Senior Editor)
"THE NEW NEIGHBORS" (ToyFare #14)
DOUG SAYS: "I loved the 'foot-in-the-door' sequence so much that I've been pitching Borg jokes ever since; I want to put the Borg in the background of a panel here, a panel there, 'assimilating' (read: stealing) stuff. They'd be at the X-Men's party 'assimilating' the punch, at Dr. Doom's garage sale 'assimilating' his change jar, or at the Academy Awards 'assimilating' that fake-ass smile people give when they don't win. Of course, nobody agrees with me and you haven't seen the Borg since *ToyFare* #14."

ZACH OAT (*ToyFare* Editor)
"SHANKS FOR THE MEMORIES" (ToyFare #56)
ZACH SAYS: "When I started as 'TTT' photographer, Pat McCallum and I acted out every scene we shot, doing terrible impersonations of the Lizard, Franklin Richards and the Red Skull, among others. Most got old fast, but the Mario Brothers panel from this prison strip, where they're portrayed as imprisoned Italian crime bosses who constantly snipe at each other, kept us in stitches for hours. The warehouse reverberated with cries of 'Shut uppa you face' and 'No, shut uppa *you* face!' To this day, we still think 'TTT' would be funnier with sound chips."

JUSTIN ACLIN (*ToyFare* Associate Editor)
"DAREDEVIL BUYS A CAR" (Daredevil ACE Edition)
JUSTIN SAYS: "I was thrilled when I was pegged to be the project leader on the 'Twisted ToyFare Theatre' episodes that go in our sister publication *Wizard*'s Marvel ACE Editions, but I forgot one very important fact—I can't draw. So while normal 'TTTs' are storyboarded by the able Tom Root or the art degree-holding Zach Oat, my drawings inevitably end up looking like they should be hung on a refrigerator with a magnet. Case in point, this panel from my storyboards for the strip 'Daredevil Buys a Car,' where I let you know I cannot draw Daredevil sitting in a car."

by Adam Patyk

YOU CAN DO IT!

MAKE YOUR OWN 'TTT,' KIDS! JUVENILE SENSE OF HUMOR NOT INCLUDED

Hey, *ToyFare* fans! Ever wanted to create your own "Twisted ToyFare Theatre" adventures, but without the hassle of paying hundreds of dollars for customized Megos? Well, now all it takes is a pair of scissors and your own puerile imagination, along with these handy cut-outs!

CENSORED

Lay's Potato Chips